GARFIELD

Classics

Volume Eleven

MY ELEVENTH CLASSIC
COLLECTION CONTAINS:

SAYS IT WITH FLOWERS

WAVE REBEL

LET'S PARTY

JIM DAVIS

(www.garfield.com)

First published by Ravette Publishing 2003.

Printed and bound in Great Britain
for Ravette Publishing Limited,
Unit 3, Tristar Centre,
Star Road, Partridge Green,
West Sussex RH13 8RA

by Cox & Wyman Ltd, Reading, Berkshire

ISBN: 1 84161 175 1

Garfield
Says It With Flowers

JIM DAVIS

© 1993 United Feature Syndicate, Inc.

© 1993 United Feature Syndicate, Inc.

© 1993 United Feature Syndicate, Inc

© 1993 United Feature Syndicate, Inc.

© 1993 United Feature Syndicate, Inc

© 1993 United Feature Syndicate, Inc

© 1993 United Feature Syndicate, Inc.

JIM DAVIS 7-16

© 1993 United Feature Syndicate, Inc.

© 1993 United Feature Syndicate, Inc

© 1993 United Feature Syndicate, Inc.

© 1993 United Feature Syndicate, Inc.

© 1993 United Feature Syndicate, Inc.

© 1993 United Feature Syndicate, Inc.

© 1993 United Feature Syndicate, Inc.

© 1993 United Feature Syndicate, Inc

© 1993 United Feature Syndicate, Inc.

© 1993 United Feature Syndicate, Inc.

© 1993 United Feature Syndicate, Inc.

© 1993 United Feature Syndicate, Inc

© 1993 United Feature Syndicate, Inc

© 1993 United Feature Syndicate, Inc.

© 1993 United Feature Syndicate, Inc.

© 1993 United Feature Syndicate, Inc.

© 1993 United Feature Syndicate, Inc.

© 1993 United Feature Syndicate, Inc

© 1993 United Feature Syndicate, Inc

© 1993 United Feature Syndicate, Inc

© 1993 United Feature Syndicate, Inc.

© 1993 United Feature Syndicate Inc

JIM DAVIS 10-12

IT'S AMAZING WHAT ONE CAN DO WITH A ROLLING PIN

1993 United Feature Syndicate Inc

Garfield

Wave
Rebel

JIM DAVIS

© 1993 United Feature Syndicate, Inc.

© 1993 United Feature Syndicate, Inc.

© 1993 United Feature Syndicate, Inc.

© 1993 United Feature Syndicate, Inc.

© 1993 United Feature Syndicate, Inc.

© 1993 United Feature Syndicate, Inc.

SOMETHING VERY TRAGIC JUST HAPPENED TO ODIE!

© 1993 United Feature Syndicate, Inc.

JIM DAVIS 11-27

SLASH!

© 1993 United Feature Syndicate, Inc.

THINKING OF YOU

JIM DAVIS 11-30

© 1993 United Feature Syndicate, Inc.

© 1993 United Feature Syndicate, Inc.

CHRISTMAS
IS COMING

© 1993 United Feature Syndicate, Inc.

JIM DAVIS 12-7

© 1993 United Feature Syndicate, Inc.

© 1993 United Feature Syndicate, Inc.

© 1993 United Feature Syndicate, Inc.

© 1993 United Feature Syndicate, Inc.

ZIP!

© 1994 United Feature Syndicate. Inc

MUNCH
MUNCH
MUNCH

SHOW-OFF

JIM DAVIS 1-11

© 1994 United Feature Syndicate, Inc.

© 1994 United Feature Syndicate, Inc.

© 1994 United Feature Syndicate, Inc.

© 1994 United Feature Syndicate, Inc.

© 1994 United Feature Syndicate. Inc

© 1994 United Feature Syndicate, Inc.

Garfield

Let's Party

JIM DAVIS

© 1994 United Feature Syndicate, Inc.

© 1994 United Feature Syndicate Inc

WHACK!

JIM DAVIS 4-21

© 1994 United Feature Syndicate, Inc.

© 1994 United Feature Syndicate, Inc.

© 1994 PAWS, INC./Distributed by Universal Press Syndicate

© 1994 PAWS, INC./Distributed by Universal Press Syndicate

© 1994 PAWS, INC /Distributed by Universal Press Syndicate

BIBUU BIBUU
BIBUU BIBUU

© 1994 PAWS, INC./Distributed by Universal Press Syndicate

© 1994 PAWS, INC./Distributed by Universal Press Syndicate

© 1994 PAWS, INC./Distributed by Universal Press Syndicate

© 1994 PAWS, INC./Distributed by Universal Press Syndicate

© 1994 PAWS, INC./Distributed by Universal Press Syndicate

OTHER GARFIELD BOOKS AVAILABLE

Pocket Books	Price	ISBN
Below Par	£3.50	1 84161 152 2
Bon Appetit	£3.50	1 84161 038 0
Eat My Dust	£3.50	1 84161 098 4
Fun in the Sun	£3.50	1 84161 097 6
The Gladiator	£3.50	1 85304 941 7
Goooooooal!	£3.50	1 84161 037 2
Great Impressions	£3.50	1 85304 191 2
In Training	£3.50	1 85304 785 6
The Irresistible	£3.50	1 85304 940 9
Light Of My Life	£3.50	1 85304 353 2
On The Right Track	£3.50	1 85304 907 7
Pop Star	£3.50	1 84161 151 4
To Eat, Or Not To Eat?	£3.50	1 85304 991 3
Wave Rebel	£3.50	1 85304 317 6
With Love From Me To You	£3.50	1 85304 392 3

Theme Books		
Guide to Behaving Badly	£4.50	1 85304 892 5
Guide to Cat Napping	£4.50	1 84161 087 9
Guide to Coffee Mornings	£4.50	1 84161 086 0
Guide to Creatures Great & Small	£3.99	1 85304 998 0
Guide to Healthy Living	£3.99	1 85304 972 7
Guide to Pigging Out	£4.50	1 85304 893 3
Guide to Romance	£3.99	1 85304 894 1
Guide to The Seasons	£3.99	1 85304 999 9
Guide to Successful Living	£3.99	1 85304 973 5

2-in-1 Theme Books		
The Gruesome Twosome	£6.99	1 84161 143 3
Out For The Couch	£6.99	1 84161 144 1

new titles now available		
Easy Does It	£6.99	1 84161 191 3
Licensed to Thrill	£6.99	1 84161 192 1

Classics		
Volume One	£5.99	1 85304 970 0
Volume Two	£5.99	1 85304 971 9
Volume Three	£5.99	1 85304 996 4
Volume Four	£5.99	1 85304 997 2
Volume Five	£5.99	1 84161 022 4
Volume Six	£5.99	1 84161 023 2
Volume Seven	£5.99	1 84161 088 7
Volume Eight	£5.99	1 84161 089 5
Volume Nine	£5.99	1 84161 149 2
Volume Ten	£5.99	1 84161 150 6